FROM ACORN to ZOO

AND EVERYTHING IN BETWEEN IN ALPHABETICAL ORDER

Copyright © 1992 by Satoshi Kitamura.
All rights reserved. Published by Scholastic Inc., 555 Broadway,
New York, NY 10012, by arrangement with Farrar, Straus & Giroux.
Printed in the U.S.A.
ISBN 0-590-48600-4

20 19 18 17 16 15 14 13 12 11   08   01 00 99

FROM ACORN to ZOO

AND EVERYTHING IN BETWEEN IN ALPHABETICAL ORDER

SATOSHI KITAMURA

SCHOLASTIC INC.

New York   Toronto   London   Auckland   Sydney

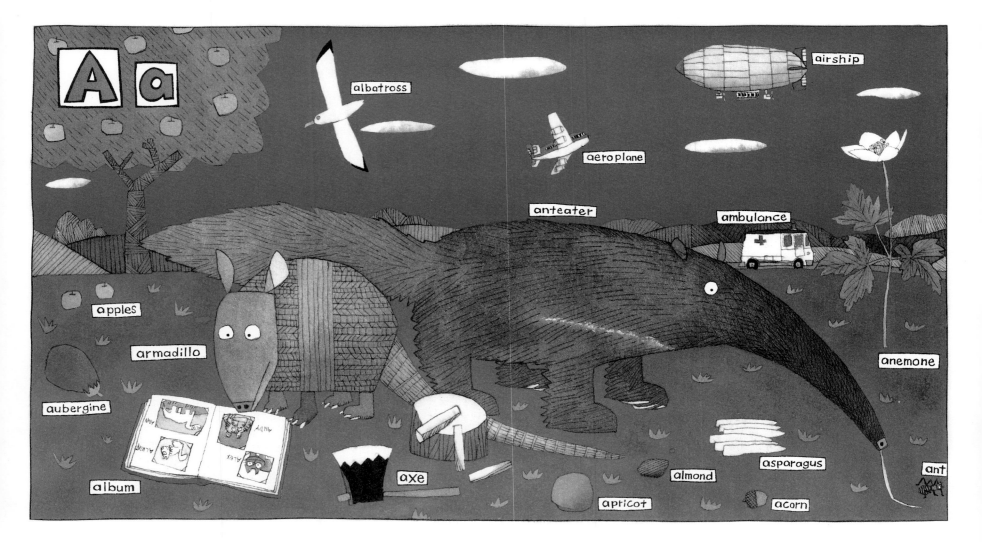

What is the armadillo balancing on his nose?

Who's watching Baby go up, up and away?

C c
crow
clock
calendar
FEBRUARY
crow
cow
chair
cat
cobra
crocodile
cactus
cabbage
crocus
candle
crayon
carrot
cherry
cabbage
clarinet
cornet
curtain
cloud
church
chimney
camel
cupboard
cucumber
can
cup
cap
cage
chameleon
cockroach

How does a cat toot a tune to charm a cobra?

8

Why should Dog
and Duck duck?!

Which came first, the eagle or the…?

With what feathered friend does Frog share his fruit?

11

What is the grinning girl holding in her hands?

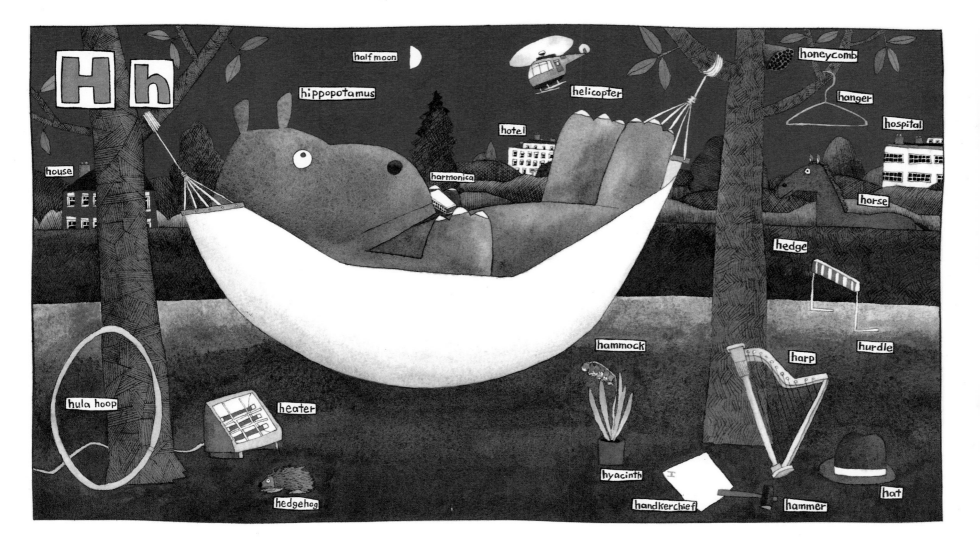

H h

half moon
honeycomb
hippopotamus
helicopter
hanger
hotel
hospital
house
harmonica
horse
hedge
hammock
harp
hurdle
hula hoop
heater
hyacinth
hedgehog
handkerchief
hammer
hat

Who's hiding in Hippo's hat?

13

iceberg

ibis

icicle

island

igloo

iron

ice cream

iris

ivory

iguana

ice

insects

ice skates

ink

How does an eager iguana
glide on the ice?

What will Jaguar enjoy for dessert?

"Who's sleeping in the kennel?" caws Kiwi.

How does Lion light up the night?

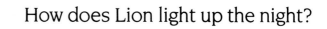

"Boo!" says the masked magpie.
Who does he scare?

What does a natty nightingale wear?

19

observatory

overcoat

owl

oar

Octopus

ostrich

otter

Onion

okra

orange

oboe

ocarina

Whooo goes out to
sea with Octopus?

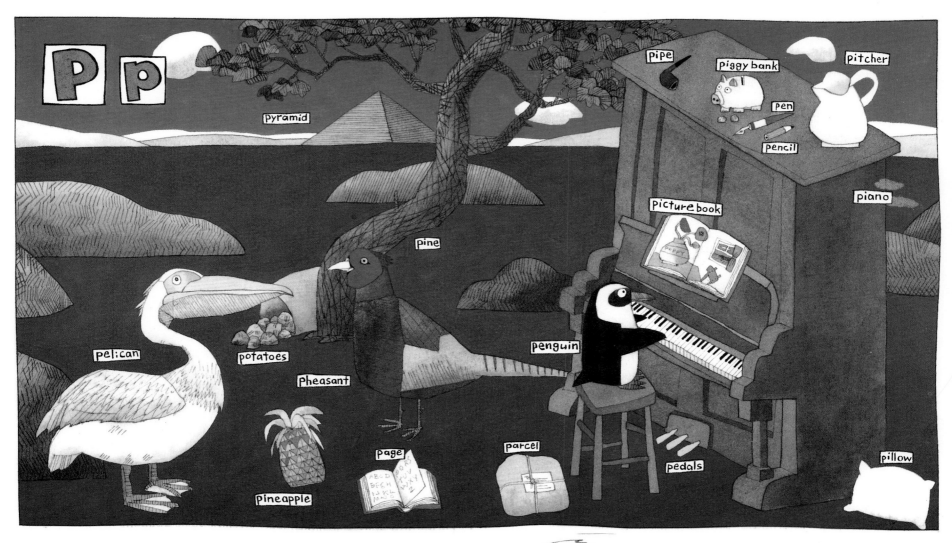

P p

pyramid

pipe

piggy bank

pitcher

pen

pencil

piano

picture book

pine

pelican

potatoes

Pheasant

penguin

pineapple

page

parcel

pedals

pillow

What is Penguin putting
in the postbox?

POST

21

What can a queen use to make her Q's?

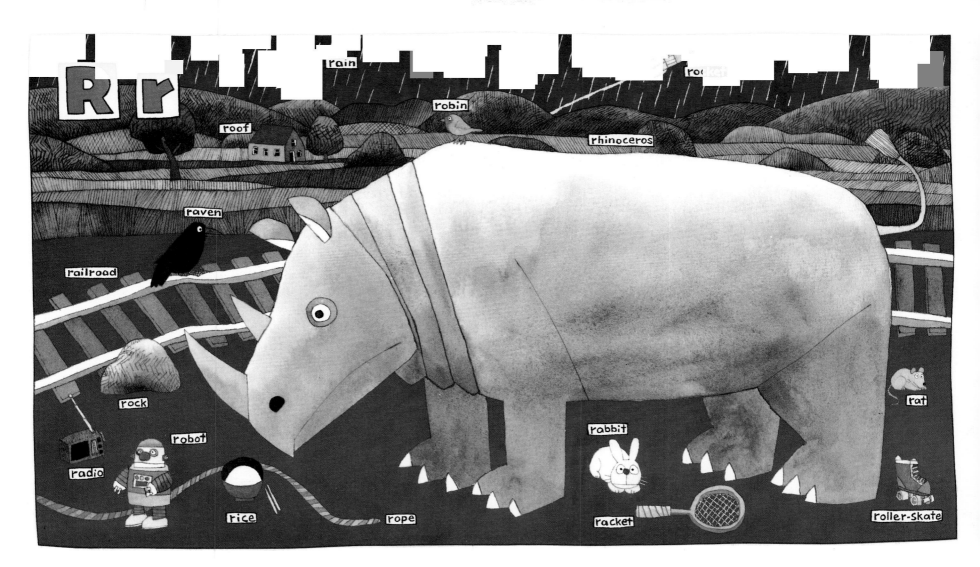

R r

rain · rock · robin · roof · rhinoceros · raven · railroad · rock · robot · radio · rice · rope · rabbit · racket · rat · roller-skate

How does Rabbit
race along the road?

What should a snazzy sea gull wear
at the seashore?

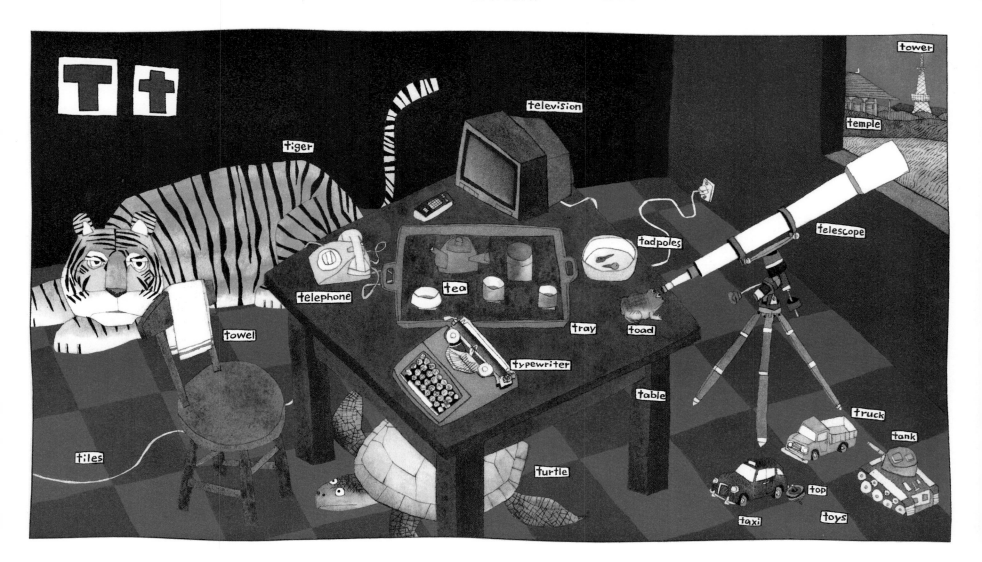

Who watches Turtle while Turtle watches television?

Up in the sky! What's coming
to visit Unicorn?

volcano

vine

Vacuum cleaner

van

vulture

violin

viper

violet

vegetables

vase

Who plays the violin like a virtuoso?

W W

walls
wings
warbler
woodpecker
wardrobe
whale
waves
willow
wolf
wallaby
walrus
watch
wheelchair
weasel
window
wool
wallet
walnut

What do Wolf and Wallaby wear to keep warm?

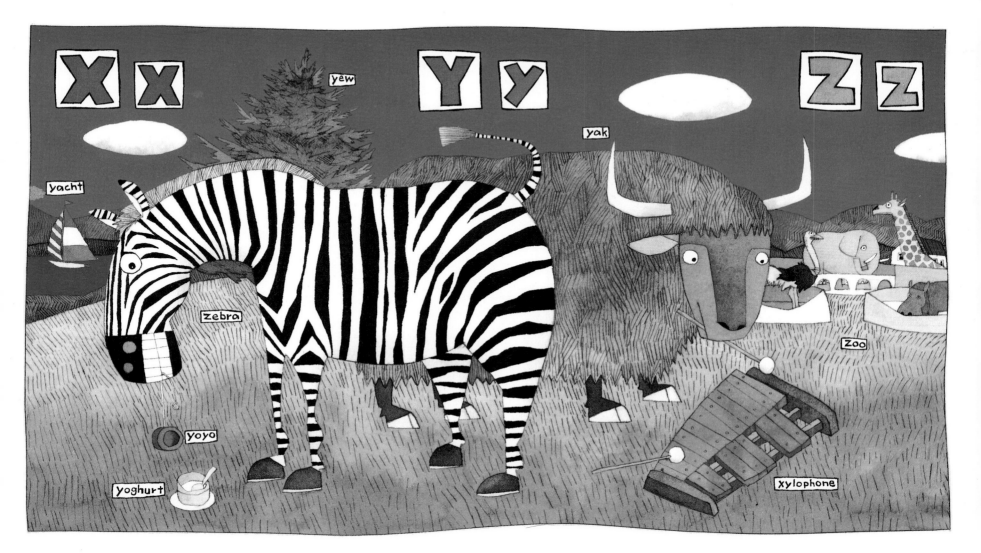

Yoohoo! Where are Zebra's friends?

29